André Leblanc

Safe and Sound

Arriving in the New World

Translated by Jane Macaulay

Smith, Bonappétit & Son

Montreal, Toronto

Legal Deposit: 4th quarter 2005
Bibliothèque nationale du Québec
Library and Archives Canada

Cataloguing in Publication Data (Canada)

Leblanc, André, 1940—
    Safe and sound: arriving in the New World / André
Leblanc; translated from the French by Jane Macauley.

(Our history in pictures)
"Most of the photographs in this book are by photographer
    William James Topley (1845, Montreal—1930, Vancouver)."
Translation of: Arrivés à bon port.
For ages 8-12.

ISBN 1-897118-04-X

    1. Immigrants—Canada—History—20th century.
2. Immigrants—Quebec (Province)—History—20th century.
3. Immigrants—Canada—History—20th century—Pictorial works.
4. Immigrants—Quebec (Province)—History—Pictorial works.
5. Quebec (Quebec)—History—Pictorial works. I. Macauley, Jane
II. Topley, William James III. Title. IV. Series.

FC409.I4L4213 2004   j325.71   C2004-907155-6

The publisher wishes to acknowledge the support of
the Canada Council for the Arts for this publishing
program. We are also thankful to the SODEC.

Safe and Sound
Arriving in the New World
Editor: Catherine Germain
Design and photo colouring: Andrée Lauzon
Copy Editor: Marie Lauzon

Distributor for Canada:
Fraser Direct
100 Armstrong Avenue
Georgetown, ON L7G 5S4

Printed in Canada by Litho Mille-Îles Ltd.

Quebec City, 1911

This book is dedicated to the
immigrant dearest to my heart and
everyone who made it possible for
this book to arrive "safe and sound."

Pierre Lebel lived in the Lower Town of Quebec City, at the foot of the "Breakneck Stairs." The house where he lived with his five sisters, his mother and his grandma Landry smelled of damp wood, even in summer. His mother and his oldest sister, Leontine, worked at Madame Giguere's millinery shop.

On this Saturday morning in April 1911, Pierre was sitting on the steps, waiting for Leontine, who was taking him to the market.

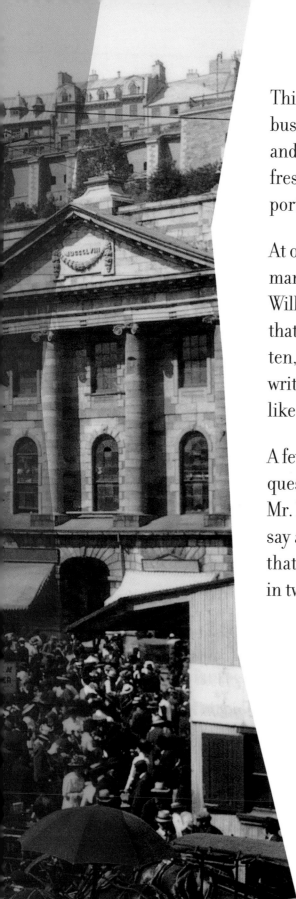

This early in the day, Champlain Market was already bustling. People shouted to one another as carts came and went. The warm smell of horses wafted on the fresh breeze from the river. The hubbub of the nearby port could be heard above the sounds of the market.

At one end of the marketplace, an elderly white-haired man was busy at work. He was the photographer, William Riley. Leontine had learned from her employer that he was looking for an assistant. Pierre, who was ten, had just finished school. He knew how to read, write and count, and was now ready to start working like a young man.

A few brief but friendly greetings were exchanged, a few questions asked, and Pierre was hired. That Monday, Mr. Riley would undertake a big contract. He didn't say anything more about it, but indicated that he would expect Pierre at his hotel in two days' time.

At 6:30 on Monday morning, Pierre was at the Blanchard Hotel, with its two little towers overlooking the now quiet square. Pierre started working with the carter, going up and down the stairs several times to load the cart that was waiting in the yard. How heavy all this photographic equipment was!

To the clip-clop of the horse's hooves, Pierre and Mr. Riley went along the city streets. The rocking motion of the cart made Pierre drowsy. He hardly bothered to look up at Laval University, crowned by its small belfry, or the tall posts that had recently been installed to supply electricity for the neighbourhood. Pierre would have liked to know where they were going, but Mr. Riley seemed sleepy too and didn't offer any information.

The two finally arrived at the Louise Basin, where the harbour station stood. So, this was their destination. The cart passed a row of moored ships, looking like fortresses that had run ashore. Pierre was excited. A ship was approaching and he could even hear the vibration of its motors. It was the *Lake Champlain*, arriving from Europe. The steamer had stopped first at Grosse Île★, where the passengers' good health was checked before they could continue their voyage to the port of Quebec. In the course of a single year, the immigrants who arrived at the port outnumbered the entire population of the city.

★ In the middle of the St. Lawrence River, downstream from Quebec City, is a rather small island called Grosse Île, where every ship had to stop for medical inspection. Few vaccines had been developed at the time, and it was feared that epidemics of diseases like cholera, typhus and smallpox might arrive with the newcomers. Anyone who was suspected of carrying a contagious disease was held for several days at the island's quarantine station.

The steamer had just moored and everyone on deck seemed to be standing stock-still. What a contrast with the bustling activity on the wharves! The silent passengers stared out at the unfamiliar landscape. These people had left everything behind—their houses, their families and their countries. Pierre was surprised to see so many children on board. He had always thought of immigrants as adults.

A sudden clang of metal made him jump. Some of the crewmen had just heaved the gangplank onto the wharf.

2389

Immigration officials went aboard. Mr. Riley nudged Pierre, indicating that they should follow. They were going aboard the ship—what an adventure! But Mr. Riley brought him back down to earth right away. They had to unpack the equipment they were carrying, install the camera on its tripod and organize the heavy glass photographic plates.

When everything was ready, Mr. Riley pointed the camera at a group of passengers. One of them, a young boy almost Pierre's age, darted away as soon as he noticed the photographer. Too late! The picture had already been taken.

Passengers from the first class cabins watched them from the upper deck. Two curious children slipped between the adults to get a better view through the guardrail.

A small group of people gathered at the ladder leading to the rear deck. Pierre couldn't understand a word of what they were saying. Mr. Riley called for an interpreter and they learned that these people came from faraway Ukraine.

Voices rose from below: the people in steerage were celebrating their arrival. They would be the last to disembark and had plenty of time to spare. Surrounded by a circle of passengers, a young woman danced to the rhythm of a string held by her friend.

It was almost noon. Mr. Riley and Pierre were about to leave the ship when they came across a tiny girl in tears. Catching sight of the approaching photographer, she stopped crying at once and huddled up against her mother. Touched, her mother smiled.

The woman had travelled from Scotland with her four children. She readily agreed to sit for another photograph, but posed more formally this time. Was she a widow? Had she come to join a friend or some member of her family?

Now they had to repack all their material. Mr. Riley
was going to have a meal with the immigration officials.
Pierre decided to take a little walk to the Upper Town.
He loved to watch the ships moving about on the river.
From his pocket, he pulled out a crust of bread and a bit
of cheese that his grandmother had wrapped up in a
clean cloth for him that morning.

In the meantime, another photographer had set up his camera. He worked for the Department of the Interior. At the entrance to the harbour station he photographed a group of girls, who removed their coats to display the uniforms they wore. They were orphans, sent to Canada by English charitable societies★ that found them jobs here as servants.

★ These charitable societies, or "Homes," as they were called, sent more than 100,000 children aged 7 to 14 to Canada between 1869 and 1920. Contrary to popular belief, most of these children—70% in fact—were not orphans. They were street children, hungry and often ill, who were put on ships without the consent of their parents.

The little boy orphans sent by the St. George Society would go to work on farms or in factories.

After lunch, Pierre joined Mr. Riley in the station hall. They set
up their equipment in a corridor along the side of the building,
where the light offered better contrast. An immigration official
introduced them to people to be photographed. Among them
were this family, the Corbetts, from Surrey, England, accompanied
by their nanny. The father had arrived the year before, and
the family would soon be reunited.

Mr. Riley prepared to take another photograph, but
more and more curious onlookers crowded in.
The throng was made to step back. The photographer was
bothered by all this commotion, not to mention a little
boy who kept moving his head. The photograph had to
be retaken several times, and the eldest sister eventually
lost her gentle smile. These were the children of a
Russian Jewish family that had fled the pogroms★.
Had they lost their parents back in their native land?

★ Pogrom: a popular uprising
against Jewish communities,
encouraged by the authorities
and accompanied by
pillaging and massacres.

The Galatians★ wore the embroidered
jackets that kept them warm during
the bitter winters back home. They had
put these clothes on for the long
voyage to their new country. They
looked as if they were going to a party.

★Galatia: a region in central
Europe, north of the Carpathian
Mountains between Krakow
(Poland) and L'viv (Ukraine).
After the First World War, this
country disappeared from the map
of Europe. It first became part of
Poland and then was divided
between Poland and Ukraine.

26

The people always arrived in small groups, huddled close together. A German family, though tired, was preparing to continue on their way to Manitoba. They had come close to being quarantined on Grosse Île. The mother had come down with a high fever, but fortunately recovered.

There was a Dutch family too. The husband, with his
rumpled pea jacket looking as if it had been worn for the
whole trip, held the precious papers that authorized him
to enter the country. His wife, with a child on her hip,
had the imperturbable look of a Madonna.

To the right of the mother in the photograph is the
interpreter, who would stand back while the photographs
were being taken. He had to know several languages,
for all these newcomers were selected exclusively from
countries where French was not the native tongue.

Mr. Riley wanted to produce fine portraits. They would be used to convince potential immigrants in various European countries that they would be well treated in Canada and find other people from their homelands. It was important work.

Mr. Riley often insisted on taking a photograph over again, because he sought a certain effect or expression. When it came to this English family with nine children, he wanted to produce a group portrait that would look as if they had all come to sit for him in his studio... with or without the father's cap.

The young boy at the window and the little girls had no one to accompany them. The interpreter managed to find out more. The boy had travelled from England alone. His name was Chadwick Sandles, and he was going to meet an uncle in Montreal. The two little Polish girls were in a more difficult situation. They had embarked on the wrong vessel at Grosse Île and were separated from their parents, who would be on the next ship.

People with disabilities, mental illness or serious diseases were usually sent back to their country of origin. The young boy on crutches would have to sail back to Liverpool.

Pierre took the equipment out into the port area so that Mr. Riley could take photographs of people departing for other destinations. Few immigrants actually stayed in Quebec City. Most of them boarded the railway ferry that would carry them across the river to Lévis. At that time, there was no bridge between the north and south shores near the city. At the Lévis train station, the train carriages would be attached to a locomotive that would take the immigrants to different places all across the country.

All these people had arrived safe and sound. A new life was beginning for them!

In the vast hall, now deserted, there still remained a little girl.
She had been told to wait and she had sat here quietly, with
her landing certificate in her hands. Her name did not match
any adult passenger's name. She was registered neither in
the list of orphans nor in the list of children travelling alone.
There was a problem, but the little girl remained silent
when people asked her questions.

As it turned out, this little girl would become Pierre's neighbour
and best friend, so he would always be touched by the memory
of this last photograph... and of his very first day of work.

PHOTO CREDITS

Cover, inside cover and p. 1: Unknown photographer, National Archives of Canada (NAC), C-37613 (details)

p. 3: W.J. Topley, NAC, PA-10223

p. 5: W. Notman & Co., NAC, PA-13129 (detail)

p. 6: Unknown, NAC, PA-21358 (detail)

p. 7: W.J. Topley, NAC, PA-43063 (detail)

p. 8: C.M. Johnston, NAC, PA-56483

p. 9: J. Woodruff, NAC, PA-20880

p. 10: W.J. Topley, NAC, PA-10100

p. 11: W.J. Topley, NAC, PA-10170

p. 12: W.J. Topley, NAC, PA-10171 (detail)

p. 13: W.J. Topley, NAC, PA-10235 (detail)

p. 14: W.J. Topley, NAC, PA-10225

p. 15: Unknown, Flaherty, NAC, PA-114940 (detail)

p. 16 (top): W.J. Topley, NAC, PA-10237

p. 16 (bottom): P. Toles, NAC, PA-127154

p. 17: Unknown, NAC, C-9660

p. 18: W.J. Topley, NAC, PA-10151

p. 19: W.J. Topley, NAC, PA-10226 (detail)

p. 20: Unknown, NAC, PA-24873

p. 22: Unknown, NAC, PA-20906

p. 23: Unknown, NAC, PA-20907

p. 24: W.J. Topley, NAC, PA-10150

p. 25 (top): W.J. Topley, NAC, PA-10409 (detail)

p. 25 (bottom): W.J. Topley, NAC, PA-10400

p. 26-27: W.J. Topley, NAC, PA-10401

p. 28: W.J. Topley, NAC, PA-10264 (detail)

p. 29: W.J. Topley, NAC, PA-10256 (detail)

p. 30-31: W.J. Topley, NAC, PA-10270

p. 32: W.J. Topley, NAC, PA-10494

p. 33: W.J. Topley, NAC, PA-10399

p. 34 (top): W.J. Topley, NAC, PA-10234

p. 34 (bottom): W.J. Topley, NAC, PA-10263 (detail)

p. 35: W.J. Topley, NAC, PA-20910 (detail)

p. 36: W.J. Topley, NAC, PA-10392

p. 37 (top): W.J. Topley, NAC, PA-8497

p. 37 (bottom): W.J. Topley, NAC, C-7758 (detail)

p. 39: Unknown, NAC, C-63254 (detail)

p. 40: Unknown, NAC, PA-48695

Our very special thanks go to the staff of the National Archives of Canada.